Golf is like a love affair.
If you don't take it seriously,
it's no fun; if you do take it seriously,
it breaks your heart.

Arnold Daly

This edition © Robert Frederick Ltd. 1996 Old Orchard Street, Bath BA1 1JU
First published 1996; All rights reserved.
Printed and bound in China

THE GOLFER'S
BOOK OF RECORDS

C E Brock

Golf is a typical capitalist lunacy of upper-class Edwardian England.

George Bernard Shaw

Golfing Records

Course ....   Date ....

Competition ....

Players ....

....

Hole	Yards	Par	Self	Opponent
1				
2				
3				
4				
5				
6				
7				
8				
9				
Out				

Competitor's Signature ....

Marker's Signature ....

Hole	Yards	Par	Self	Opponent
10				
11				
12				
13				
14				
15				
16				
17				
18				
In				
Out				
Total				
Handicap				
Net Score				

Golfing Records

Course .... Date ....

Competition ....

Players ....

....

Hole	Yards	Par	Self	Opponent
1				
2				
3				
4				
5				
6				
7				
8				
9				
Out				

Hole	Yards	Par	Self	Opponent
10				
11				
12				
13				
14				
15				
16				
17				
18				
In				
Out				
Total				
Handicap				
Net Score				

Competitor's
Signature ....

Marker's
Signature ....

Golfing Records

Course ....   Date ....

Competition ....

Players ....

....

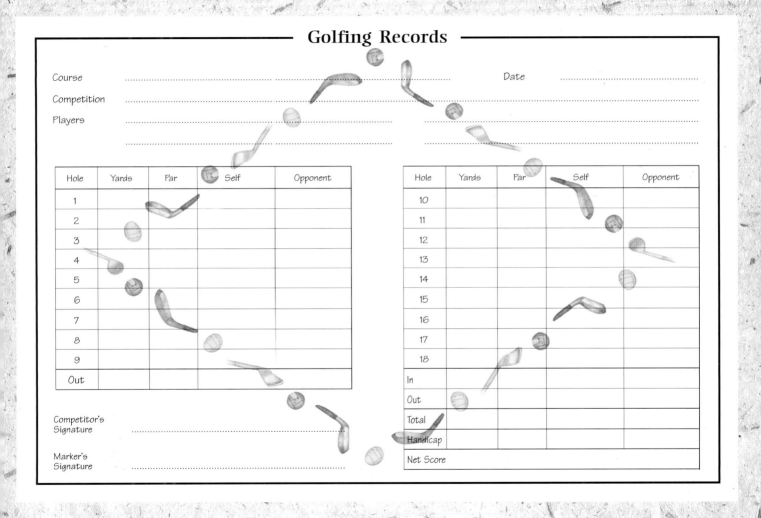

Hole	Yards	Par	Self	Opponent
1				
2				
3				
4				
5				
6				
7				
8				
9				
Out				

Hole	Yards	Par	Self	Opponent
10				
11				
12				
13				
14				
15				
16				
17				
18				
In				
Out				
Total				
Handicap				
Net Score				

Competitor's Signature ....

Marker's Signature ....

Golfing Records

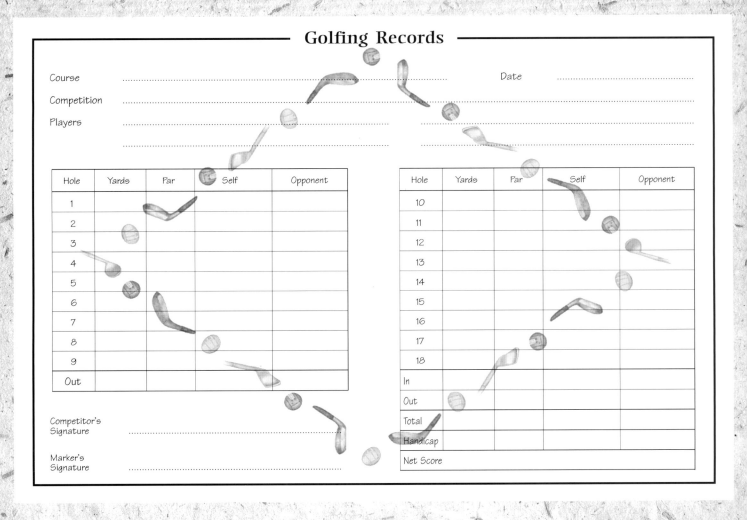

Course .... Date ....

Competition ....

Players ....

....

Hole	Yards	Par	Self	Opponent
1				
2				
3				
4				
5				
6				
7				
8				
9				
Out				

Hole	Yards	Par	Self	Opponent
10				
11				
12				
13				
14				
15				
16				
17				
18				
In				
Out				
Total				
Handicap				
Net Score				

Competitor's Signature ....

Marker's Signature ....

Golfing Records

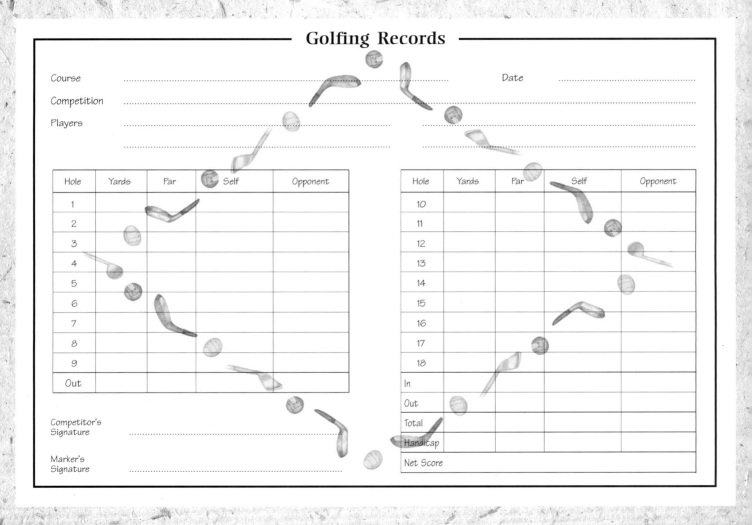

Course .... **Date** ....

Competition ....

Players ....

....

Hole	Yards	Par	Self	Opponent
1				
2				
3				
4				
5				
6				
7				
8				
9				
Out				

Competitor's Signature ....

Marker's Signature ....

Hole	Yards	Par	Self	Opponent
10				
11				
12				
13				
14				
15				
16				
17				
18				
In				
Out				
Total				
Handicap				
Net Score				

Golfing Records

Course ....   Date ....

Competition ....

Players ....

....

Hole	Yards	Par	Self	Opponent
1				
2				
3				
4				
5				
6				
7				
8				
9				
Out				

Hole	Yards	Par	Self	Opponent
10				
11				
12				
13				
14				
15				
16				
17				
18				
In				
Out				
Total				
Handicap				
Net Score				

Competitor's
Signature ....

Marker's
Signature ....

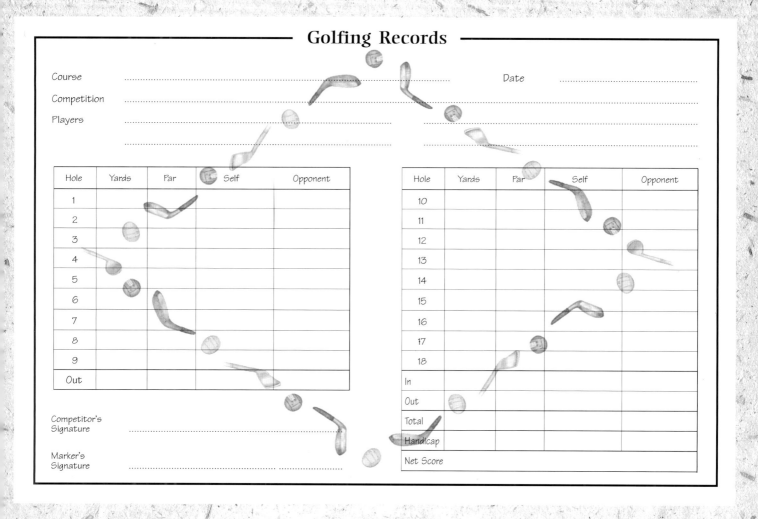

Golfing Records

Course ....

Competition ....

Players ....

....

Date ....

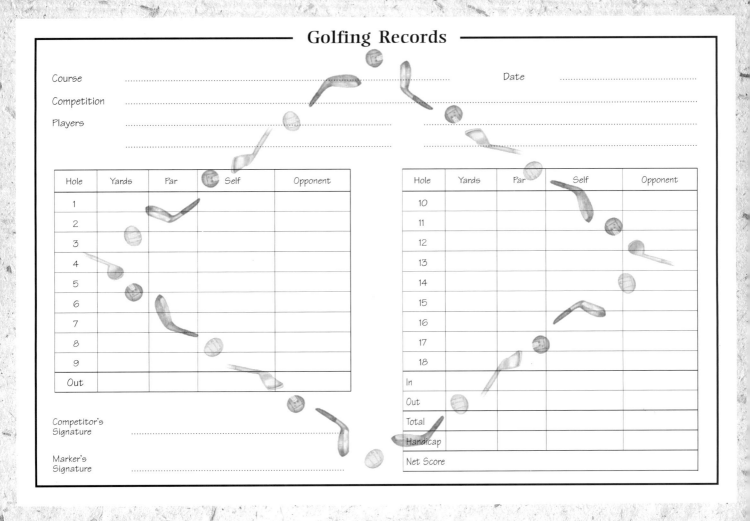

Hole	Yards	Par	Self	Opponent
1				
2				
3				
4				
5				
6				
7				
8				
9				
Out				

Hole	Yards	Par	Self	Opponent
10				
11				
12				
13				
14				
15				
16				
17				
18				
In				
Out				
Total				
Handicap				
Net Score				

Competitor's
Signature ....

Marker's
Signature ....

Golfing Records

Course .... Date ....

Competition ....

Players ....

....

Hole	Yards	Par	Self	Opponent
1				
2				
3				
4				
5				
6				
7				
8				
9				
Out				

Competitor's Signature ....

Marker's Signature ....

Hole	Yards	Par	Self	Opponent
10				
11				
12				
13				
14				
15				
16				
17				
18				
In				
Out				
Total				
Handicap				
Net Score				

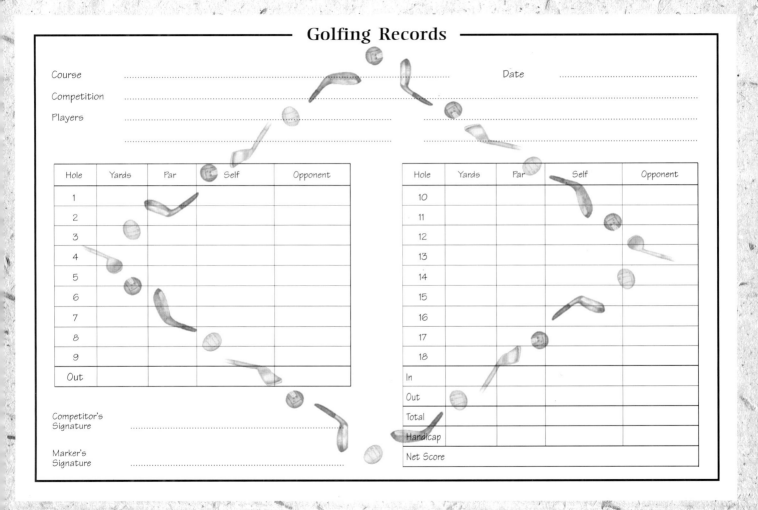

PHILOSOPHER (*eight down to bogey*). "Anyway I don't suppose for one moment the cup is real silver."

You hit the ball and if it doesn't go far enough you just hit it again, and if that doesn't work, you hit it again, and so on.

Robert Robinson

Golfing Records

Course .... Date ....

Competition ....

Players ....

....

Hole	Yards	Par	Self	Opponent
1				
2				
3				
4				
5				
6				
7				
8				
9				
Out				

Competitor's Signature ....

Marker's Signature ....

Hole	Yards	Par	Self	Opponent
10				
11				
12				
13				
14				
15				
16				
17				
18				
In				
Out				
Total				
Handicap				
Net Score				

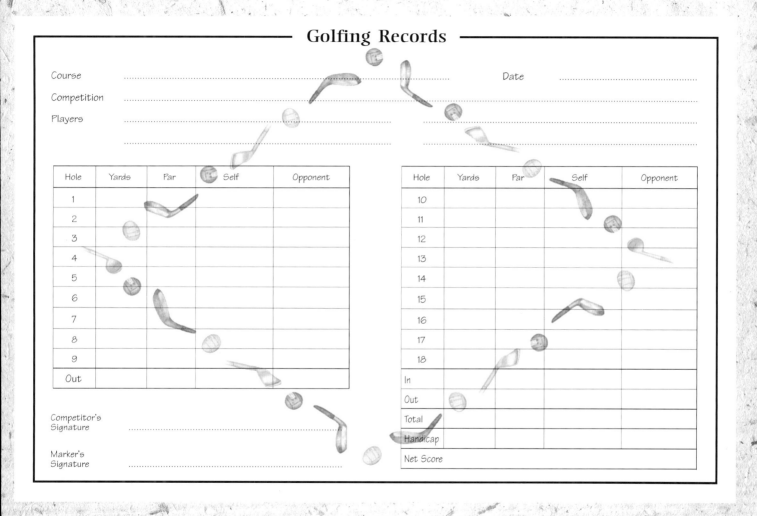

Golfing Records

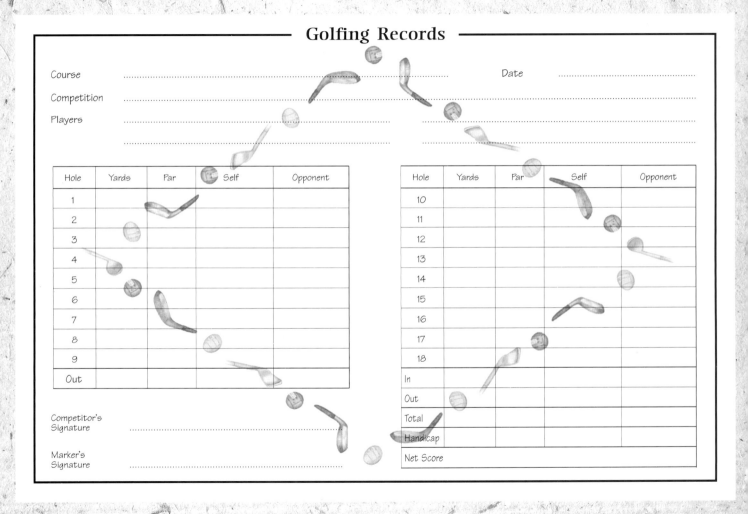

Course ....   Date ....

Competition ....

Players ....

....

Hole	Yards	Par	Self	Opponent
1				
2				
3				
4				
5				
6				
7				
8				
9				
Out				

Hole	Yards	Par	Self	Opponent
10				
11				
12				
13				
14				
15				
16				
17				
18				
In				
Out				
Total				
Handicap				
Net Score				

Competitor's Signature ....

Marker's Signature ....

Golfing Records

Course ....   Date ....

Competition ....

Players ....

....

Hole	Yards	Par	Self	Opponent
1				
2				
3				
4				
5				
6				
7				
8				
9				
Out				

Hole	Yards	Par	Self	Opponent
10				
11				
12				
13				
14				
15				
16				
17				
18				
In				
Out				
Total				
Handicap				
Net Score				

Competitor's Signature ....

Marker's Signature ....

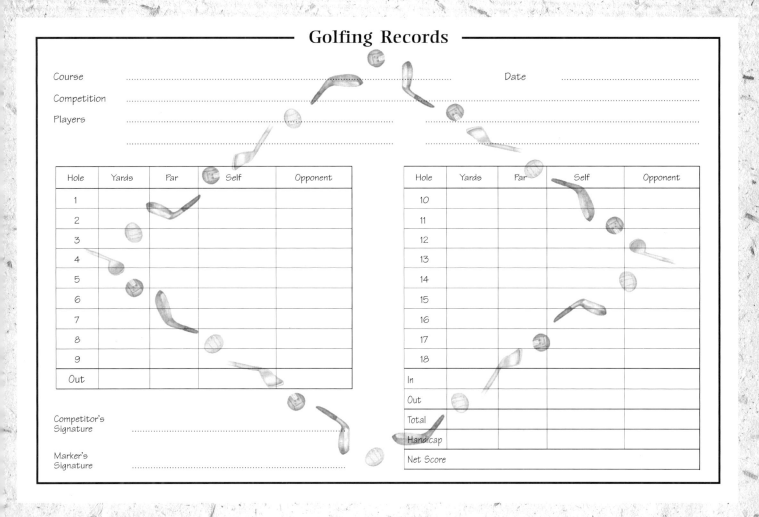

Golfing Records

Course .... Date ....

Competition ....

Players ....

....

Hole	Yards	Par	Self	Opponent
1				
2				
3				
4				
5				
6				
7				
8				
9				
Out				

Hole	Yards	Par	Self	Opponent
10				
11				
12				
13				
14				
15				
16				
17				
18				
In				
Out				
Total				
Handicap				
Net Score				

Competitor's Signature ....

Marker's Signature ....

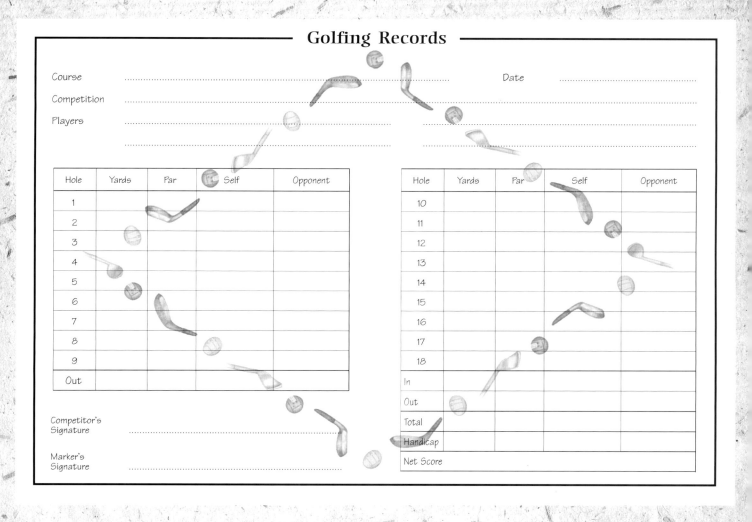

If you watch a game, it's fun.
If you play it, it's recreation.
If you work at it, it's golf.

Bob Hope

Golfing Records

Course ....

Competition ....

Players ....

....

Date ....

Hole	Yards	Par	Self	Opponent
1				
2				
3				
4				
5				
6				
7				
8				
9				
Out				

Hole	Yards	Par	Self	Opponent
10				
11				
12				
13				
14				
15				
16				
17				
18				
In				
Out				
Total				
Handicap				
Net Score				

Competitor's Signature ....

Marker's Signature ....

Golfing Records

Course ....   Date ....

Competition ....

Players ....

....

Hole	Yards	Par	Self	Opponent
1				
2				
3				
4				
5				
6				
7				
8				
9				
Out				

Hole	Yards	Par	Self	Opponent
10				
11				
12				
13				
14				
15				
16				
17				
18				
In				
Out				
Total				
Handicap				
Net Score				

Competitor's Signature ....

Marker's Signature ....

Golfing Records

Course ....

Competition ....

Players ....

....

Date ....

Hole	Yards	Par	Self	Opponent
1				
2				
3				
4				
5				
6				
7				
8				
9				
Out				

Hole	Yards	Par	Self	Opponent
10				
11				
12				
13				
14				
15				
16				
17				
18				
In				
Out				
Total				
Handicap				
Net Score				

Competitor's Signature ....

Marker's Signature ....

Golfing Records

Course .... Date ....

Competition ....

Players ....

....

Hole	Yards	Par	Self	Opponent
1				
2				
3				
4				
5				
6				
7				
8				
9				
Out				

Competitor's Signature ....

Marker's Signature ....

Hole	Yards	Par	Self	Opponent
10				
11				
12				
13				
14				
15				
16				
17				
18				
In				
Out				
Total				
Handicap				
Net Score				

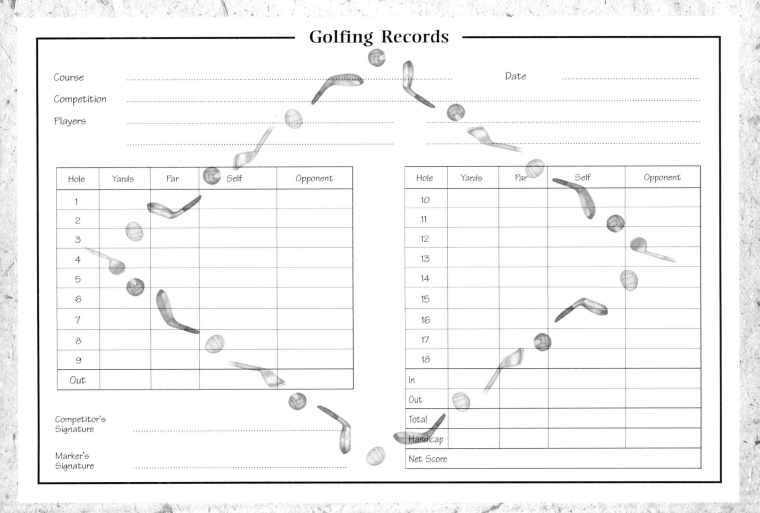

Golfing Records

Course .... Date ....

Competition ....

Players ....

....

Hole	Yards	Par	Self	Opponent
1				
2				
3				
4				
5				
6				
7				
8				
9				
Out				

Competitor's Signature ....

Marker's Signature ....

Hole	Yards	Par	Self	Opponent
10				
11				
12				
13				
14				
15				
16				
17				
18				
In				
Out				
Total				
Handicap				
Net Score				

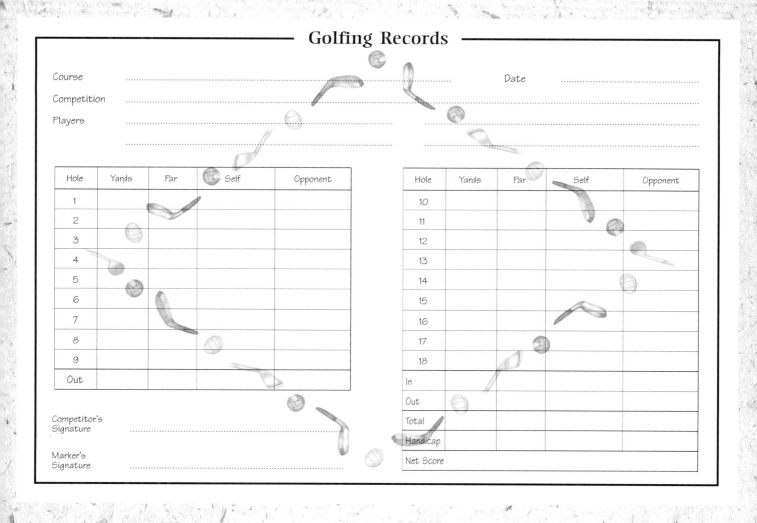

Golfing Records

Course ....

Competition ....

Players ....

....

Date ....

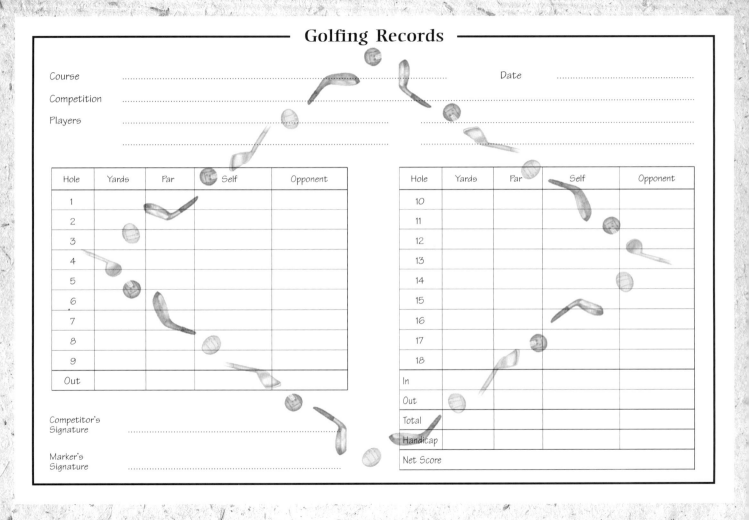

Hole	Yards	Par	Self	Opponent
1				
2				
3				
4				
5				
6				
7				
8				
9				
Out				

Competitor's Signature ....

Marker's Signature ....

Hole	Yards	Par	Self	Opponent
10				
11				
12				
13				
14				
15				
16				
17				
18				
In				
Out				
Total				
Handicap				
Net Score				

Golfing Records

Course ....   Date ....

Competition ....

Players ....

....

Hole	Yards	Par	Self	Opponent
1				
2				
3				
4				
5				
6				
7				
8				
9				
Out				

Competitor's Signature ....

Marker's Signature ....

Hole	Yards	Par	Self	Opponent
10				
11				
12				
13				
14				
15				
16				
17				
18				
In				
Out				
Total				
Handicap				
Net Score				

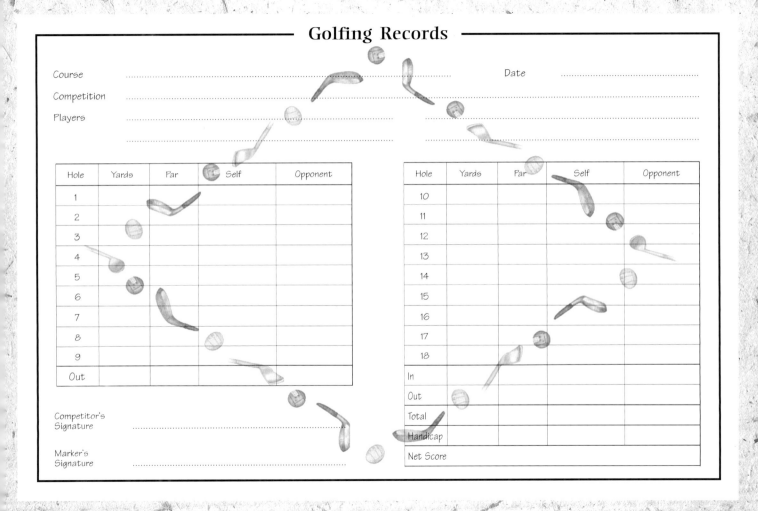

Golfing Records

Course .... Date ....

Competition ....

Players ....

....

Hole	Yards	Par	Self	Opponent
1				
2				
3				
4				
5				
6				
7				
8				
9				
Out				

Hole	Yards	Par	Self	Opponent
10				
11				
12				
13				
14				
15				
16				
17				
18				
In				
Out				
Total				
Handicap				
Net Score				

Competitor's
Signature ....

Marker's
Signature ....

Most golfers prepare for disaster.
A good golfer prepares for success.

Bob Toski

Golfing Records

Course .... Date ....

Competition ....

Players ....

....

Hole	Yards	Par	Self	Opponent
1				
2				
3				
4				
5				
6				
7				
8				
9				
Out				

Hole	Yards	Par	Self	Opponent
10				
11				
12				
13				
14				
15				
16				
17				
18				
In				
Out				
Total				
Handicap				
Net Score				

Competitor's Signature ....

Marker's Signature ....

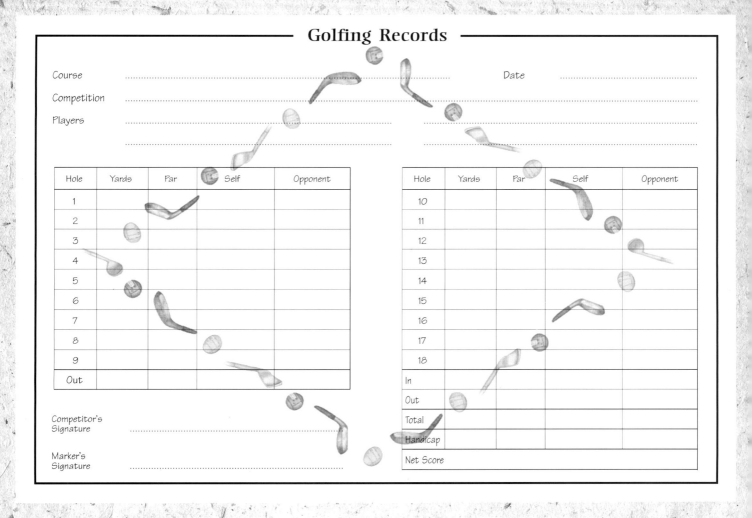

Golfing Records

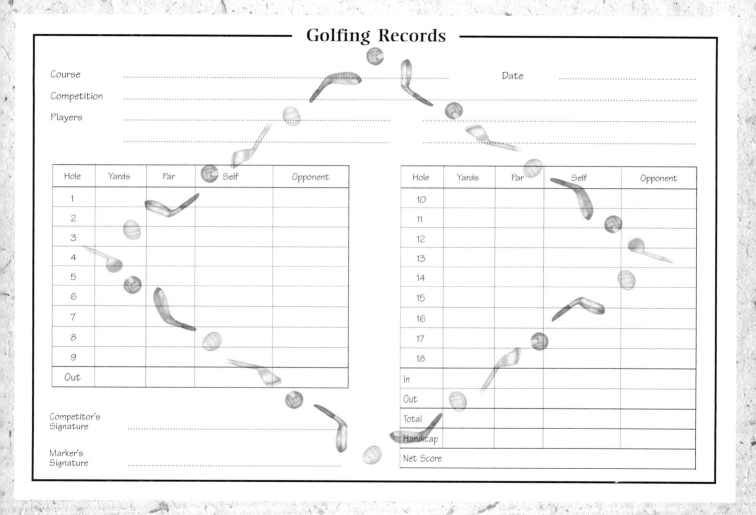

Course .... Date ....

Competition ....

Players ....

....

Hole	Yards	Par	Self	Opponent
1				
2				
3				
4				
5				
6				
7				
8				
9				
Out				

Hole	Yards	Par	Self	Opponent
10				
11				
12				
13				
14				
15				
16				
17				
18				
In				
Out				
Total				
Handicap				
Net Score				

Competitor's
Signature ....

Marker's
Signature ....

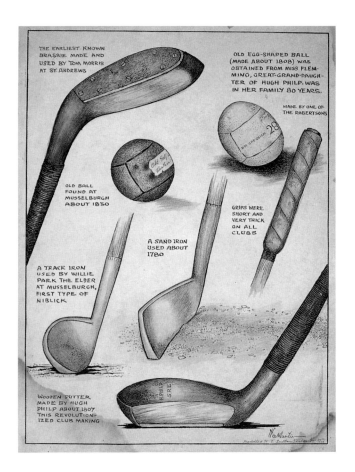

THE EARLIEST KNOWN BRASSIE MADE AND USED BY TOM MORRIS AT ST ANDREWS

OLD EGG-SHAPED BALL (MADE ABOUT 1808) WAS OBTAINED FROM MISS FLEM-MINO, GREAT-GRAND-DAUGH-TER OF HUGH PHILP. WAS IN HER FAMILY 80 YEARS.

MADE BY ONE OF THE ROBERTSONS

OLD BALL FOUND AT MUSSELBURGH ABOUT 1830

GRIPS WERE SHORT AND VERY THICK ON ALL CLUBS

A SAND IRON USED ABOUT 1780

A TRACK IRON USED BY WILLIE PARK THE ELDER AT MUSSELBURGH, FIRST TYPE OF NIBLICK

WOODEN PUTTER MADE BY HUGH PHILP ABOUT 1807 THIS REVOLUTION-IZED CLUB MAKING

Golf is a game whose aim is to hit a very small ball into an even smaller hole, with weapons singularly ill-designed for the purpose.

Sir Winston Churchill

Golfing Records

Course .... Date ....

Competition ....

Players ....

....

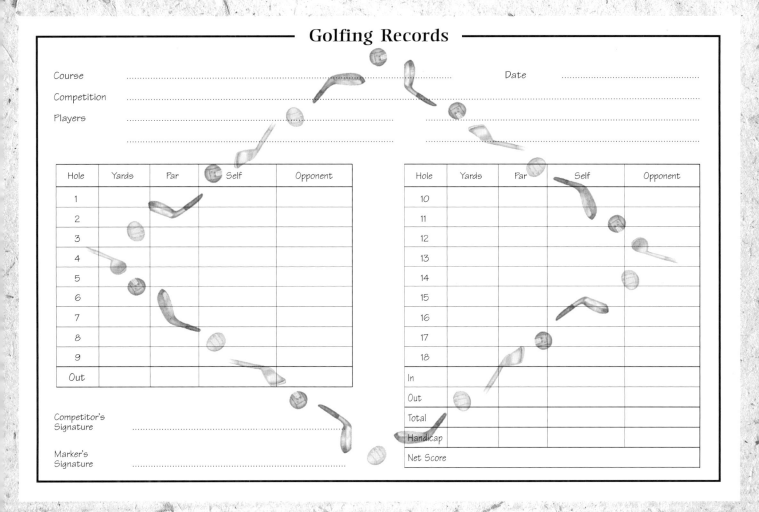

Hole	Yards	Par	Self	Opponent
1				
2				
3				
4				
5				
6				
7				
8				
9				
Out				

Hole	Yards	Par	Self	Opponent
10				
11				
12				
13				
14				
15				
16				
17				
18				
In				
Out				
Total				
Handicap				
Net Score				

Competitor's
Signature ....

Marker's
Signature ....

Golfing Records

Course ....

Date ....

Competition ....

Players ....

....

Hole	Yards	Par	Self	Opponent
1				
2				
3				
4				
5				
6				
7				
8				
9				
Out				

Hole	Yards	Par	Self	Opponent
10				
11				
12				
13				
14				
15				
16				
17				
18				
In				
Out				
Total				
Handicap				
Net Score				

Competitor's
Signature ....

Marker's
Signature ....

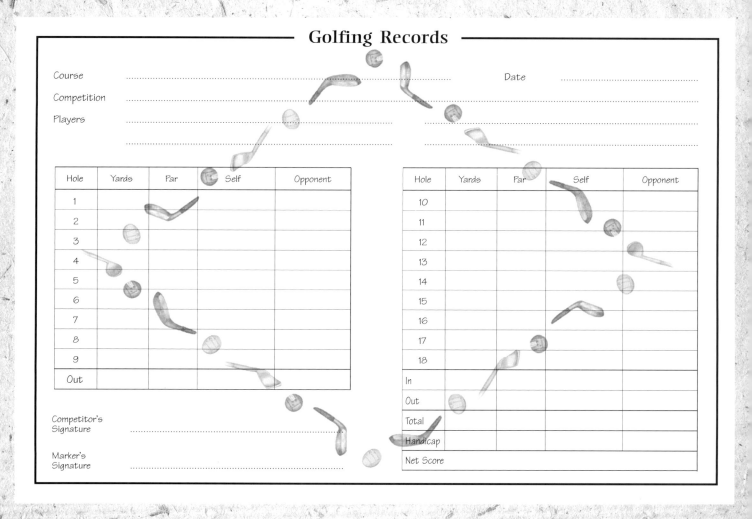

Golfing Records

Course .... Date ....

Competition ....

Players ....

....

Hole	Yards	Par	Self	Opponent
1				
2				
3				
4				
5				
6				
7				
8				
9				
Out				

Hole	Yards	Par	Self	Opponent
10				
11				
12				
13				
14				
15				
16				
17				
18				
In				
Out				
Total				
Handicap				
Net Score				

Competitor's
Signature ....

Marker's
Signature ....

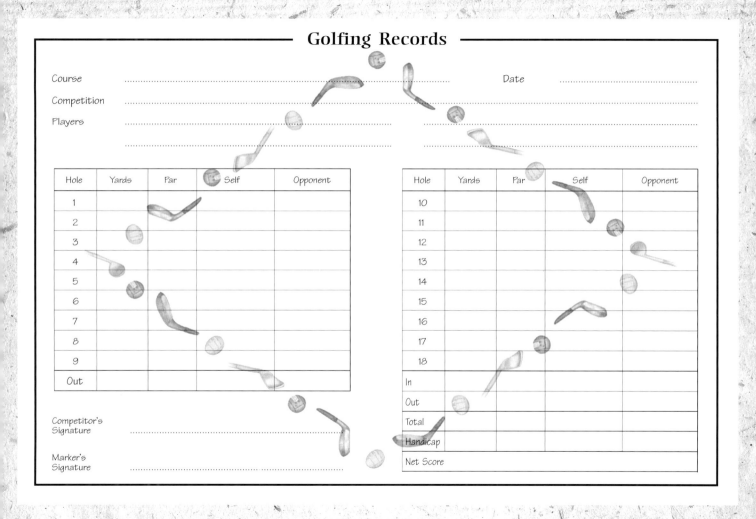

Golfing Records

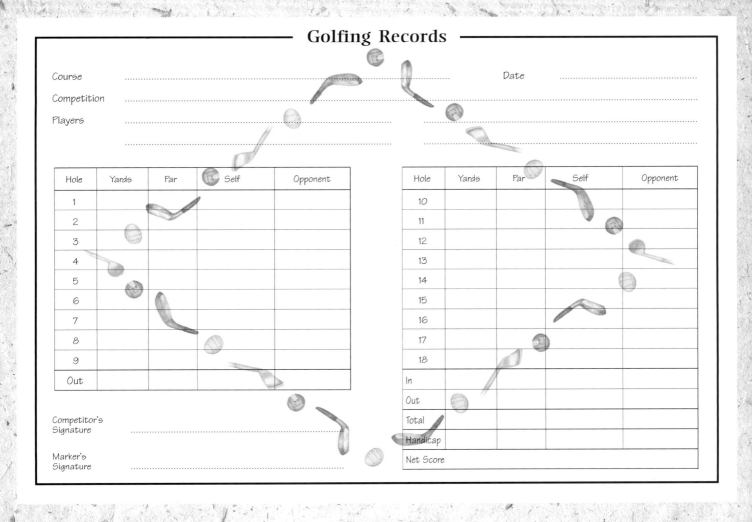

Course ....

Date ....

Competition ....

Players ....

....

Hole	Yards	Par	Self	Opponent
1				
2				
3				
4				
5				
6				
7				
8				
9				
Out				

Hole	Yards	Par	Self	Opponent
10				
11				
12				
13				
14				
15				
16				
17				
18				
In				
Out				
Total				
Handicap				
Net Score				

Competitor's
Signature ....

Marker's
Signature ....

Golfing Records

Course ....   Date ....

Competition ....

Players ....

....

Hole	Yards	Par	Self	Opponent
1				
2				
3				
4				
5				
6				
7				
8				
9				
Out				

Hole	Yards	Par	Self	Opponent
10				
11				
12				
13				
14				
15				
16				
17				
18				
In				
Out				
Total				
Handicap				
Net Score				

Competitor's
Signature ....

Marker's
Signature ....

Golfing Records

Course ....   Date ....

Competition ....

Players ....

....

Hole	Yards	Par	Self	Opponent
1				
2				
3				
4				
5				
6				
7				
8				
9				
Out				

Hole	Yards	Par	Self	Opponent
10				
11				
12				
13				
14				
15				
16				
17				
18				
In				
Out				
Total				
Handicap				
Net Score				

Competitor's
Signature ....

Marker's
Signature ....

Golfing Records

Course .... Date ....

Competition ....

Players ....

....

Hole	Yards	Par	Self	Opponent
1				
2				
3				
4				
5				
6				
7				
8				
9				
Out				

Hole	Yards	Par	Self	Opponent
10				
11				
12				
13				
14				
15				
16				
17				
18				
In				
Out				
Total				
Handicap				
Net Score				

Competitor's Signature ....

Marker's Signature ....

Golfing Records

Course .... Date ....

Competition ....

Players ....

....

Hole	Yards	Par	Self	Opponent
1				
2				
3				
4				
5				
6				
7				
8				
9				
Out				

Competitor's Signature ....

Marker's Signature ....

Hole	Yards	Par	Self	Opponent
10				
11				
12				
13				
14				
15				
16				
17				
18				
In				
Out				
Total				
Handicap				
Net Score				

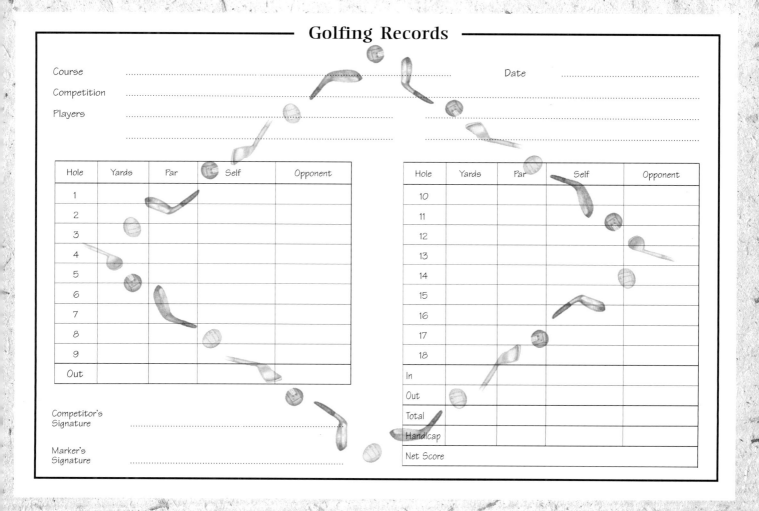

CADDIE (*as famous surgeon misses another short putt*). "Lummy! fancy bein'
operated on by '*im*!"

No man has mastered golf until he has
realised that his good shots are accidents
and his bad shots good exercise.

Eugene R Black

Golfing Records

Course	....	Date ....
Competition	....	
Players	....	
	....	

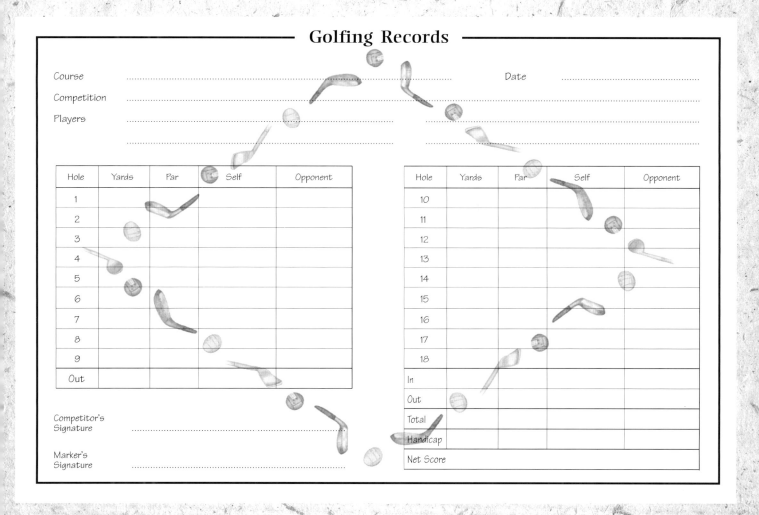

Hole	Yards	Par	Self	Opponent
1				
2				
3				
4				
5				
6				
7				
8				
9				
Out				

Hole	Yards	Par	Self	Opponent
10				
11				
12				
13				
14				
15				
16				
17				
18				
In				
Out				
Total				
Handicap				
Net Score				

Competitor's Signature ....

Marker's Signature ....

Golfing Records

Course .... Date ....

Competition ....

Players ....

....

Hole	Yards	Par	Self	Opponent
1				
2				
3				
4				
5				
6				
7				
8				
9				
Out				

Hole	Yards	Par	Self	Opponent
10				
11				
12				
13				
14				
15				
16				
17				
18				
In				
Out				
Total				
Handicap				
Net Score				

Competitor's
Signature ....

Marker's
Signature ....

Golfing Records

Course .... Date ....

Competition ....

Players ....

....

Hole	Yards	Par	Self	Opponent
1				
2				
3				
4				
5				
6				
7				
8				
9				
Out				

Competitor's Signature ....

Marker's Signature ....

Hole	Yards	Par	Self	Opponent
10				
11				
12				
13				
14				
15				
16				
17				
18				
In				
Out				
Total				
Handicap				
Net Score				

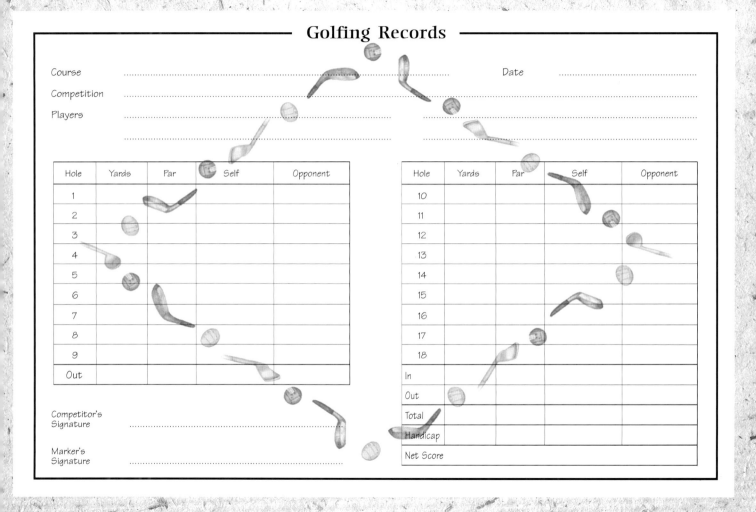

Golfing Records

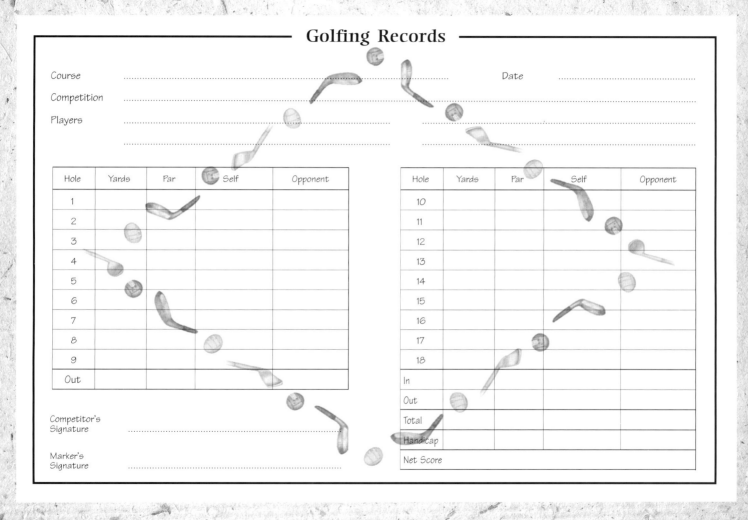

Course .... Date ....

Competition ....

Players ....

....

Hole	Yards	Par	Self	Opponent
1				
2				
3				
4				
5				
6				
7				
8				
9				
Out				

Competitor's Signature ....

Marker's Signature ....

Hole	Yards	Par	Self	Opponent
10				
11				
12				
13				
14				
15				
16				
17				
18				
In				
Out				
Total				
Handicap				
Net Score				

Golf is like art;
it's impossible to be perfect.
Sandra Palmer

Golfing Records

Course ....   Date ....

Competition ....

Players ....

....

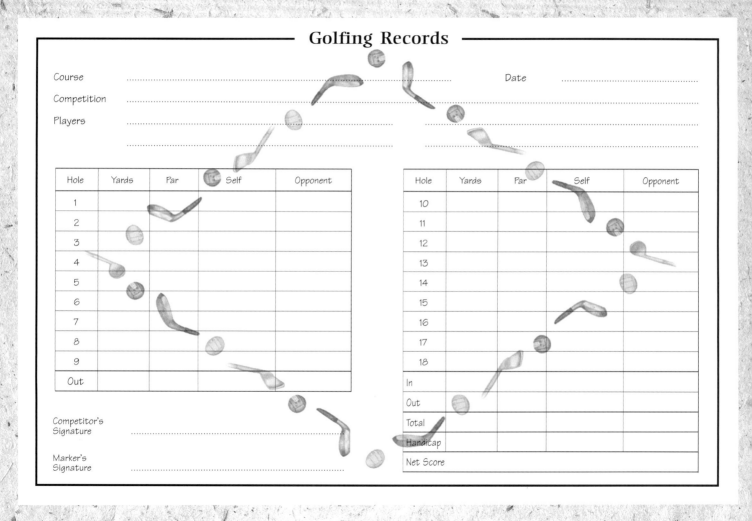

Hole	Yards	Par	Self	Opponent
1				
2				
3				
4				
5				
6				
7				
8				
9				
Out				

Hole	Yards	Par	Self	Opponent
10				
11				
12				
13				
14				
15				
16				
17				
18				
In				
Out				
Total				
Handicap				
Net Score				

Competitor's
Signature ....

Marker's
Signature ....

Golfing Records

Course .... Date ....

Competition ....

Players ....

....

Hole	Yards	Par	Self	Opponent
1				
2				
3				
4				
5				
6				
7				
8				
9				
Out				

Competitor's
Signature ....

Marker's
Signature ....

Hole	Yards	Par	Self	Opponent
10				
11				
12				
13				
14				
15				
16				
17				
18				
In				
Out				
Total				
Handicap				
Net Score				

Golfing Records

Course .... Date ....

Competition ....

Players ....

....

Hole	Yards	Par	Self	Opponent
1				
2				
3				
4				
5				
6				
7				
8				
9				
Out				

Hole	Yards	Par	Self	Opponent
10				
11				
12				
13				
14				
15				
16				
17				
18				
In				
Out				
Total				
Handicap				
Net Score				

Competitor's Signature ....

Marker's Signature ....

Golfing Records

Course .... Date ....

Competition ....

Players ....

....

Hole	Yards	Par	Self	Opponent
1				
2				
3				
4				
5				
6				
7				
8				
9				
Out				

Hole	Yards	Par	Self	Opponent
10				
11				
12				
13				
14				
15				
16				
17				
18				
In				
Out				
Total				
Handicap				
Net Score				

Competitor's Signature ....

Marker's Signature ....

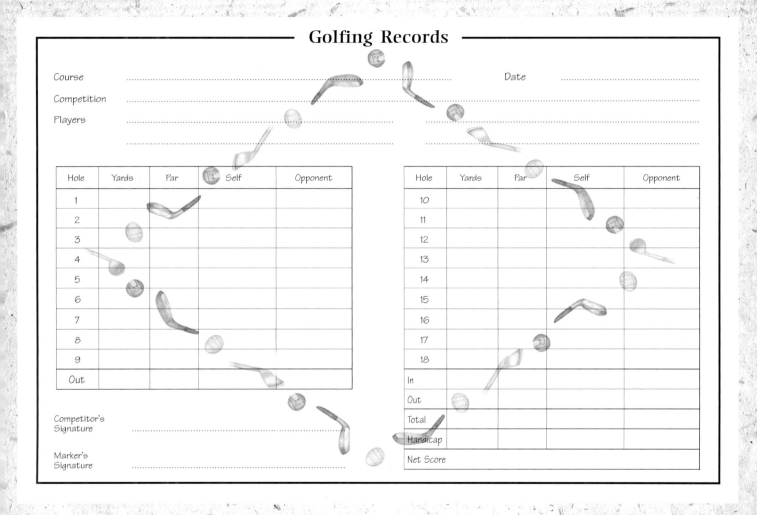

Golfing Records

Course .... Date ....

Competition ....

Players ....

....

Hole	Yards	Par	Self	Opponent
1				
2				
3				
4				
5				
6				
7				
8				
9				
Out				

Hole	Yards	Par	Self	Opponent
10				
11				
12				
13				
14				
15				
16				
17				
18				
In				
Out				
Total				
Handicap				
Net Score				

Competitor's Signature ....

Marker's Signature ....

Golfing Records

Course .... Date ....

Competition ....

Players ....

....

Hole	Yards	Par	Self	Opponent
1				
2				
3				
4				
5				
6				
7				
8				
9				
Out				

Hole	Yards	Par	Self	Opponent
10				
11				
12				
13				
14				
15				
16				
17				
18				
In				
Out				
Total				
Handicap				
Net Score				

Competitor's
Signature ....

Marker's
Signature ....

Golfing Records

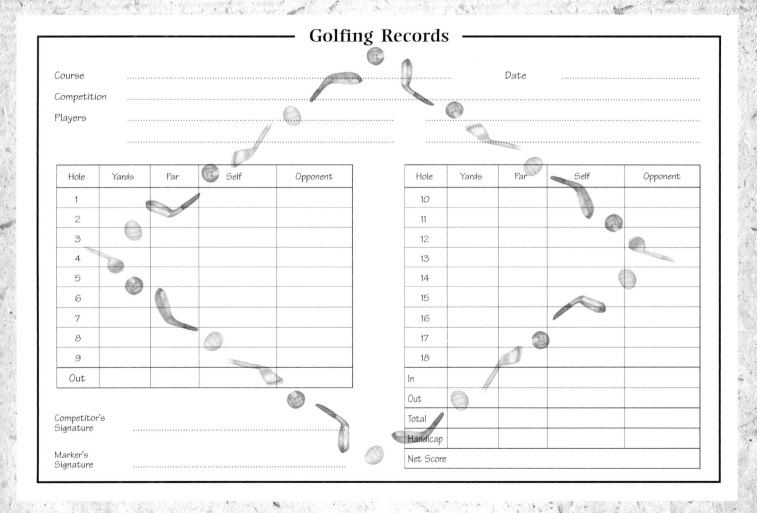

Course .... Date ....

Competition ....

Players ....

....

Hole	Yards	Par	Self	Opponent
1				
2				
3				
4				
5				
6				
7				
8				
9				
Out				

Hole	Yards	Par	Self	Opponent
10				
11				
12				
13				
14				
15				
16				
17				
18				
In				
Out				
Total				
Handicap				
Net Score				

Competitor's
Signature ....

Marker's
Signature ....

Golfing Records

Course .... Date ....

Competition ....

Players ....

....

Hole	Yards	Par	Self	Opponent
1				
2				
3				
4				
5				
6				
7				
8				
9				
Out				

Hole	Yards	Par	Self	Opponent
10				
11				
12				
13				
14				
15				
16				
17				
18				
In				
Out				
Total				
Handicap				
Net Score				

Competitor's Signature ....

Marker's Signature ....

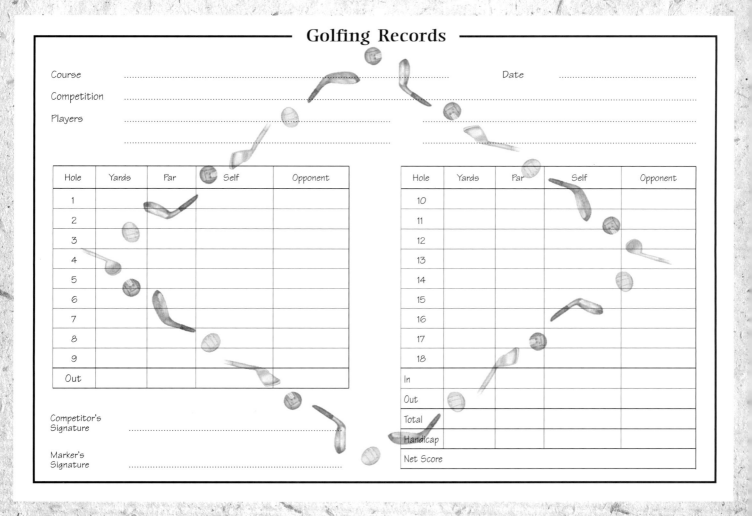

The little white ball won't move until you've hit it, and there's nothing you can do after it has gone.

Babe Didrikson Zaharias

HEART-BROKEN COMPETITOR (*who has missed a quick putt*). "Now wouldn't you call that provoking?"
CADDIE. "Well, Miss, that's a word I don't use meself."

Golfing Records

Course ....   Date ....

Competition ....

Players ....

....

Hole	Yards	Par	Self	Opponent
1				
2				
3				
4				
5				
6				
7				
8				
9				
Out				

Hole	Yards	Par	Self	Opponent
10				
11				
12				
13				
14				
15				
16				
17				
18				
In				
Out				
Total				
Handicap				
Net Score				

Competitor's Signature ....

Marker's Signature ....

Golfing Records

Course .... Date ....

Competition ....

Players ....

....

Hole	Yards	Par	Self	Opponent
1				
2				
3				
4				
5				
6				
7				
8				
9				
Out				

Competitor's
Signature ....

Marker's
Signature ....

Hole	Yards	Par	Self	Opponent
10				
11				
12				
13				
14				
15				
16				
17				
18				
In				
Out				
Total				
Handicap				
Net Score				

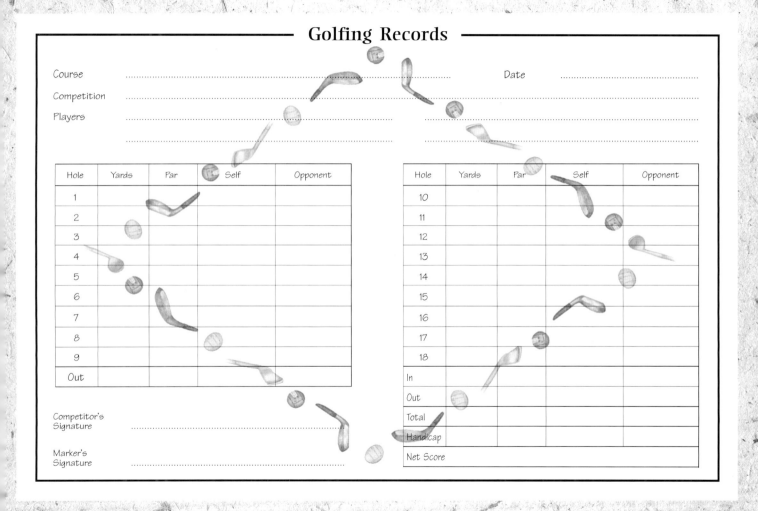

Acknowledgements:

'Copies Golfers', Edwardian Cigarette Cards in an Album
Private Collection/Bridgeman Art Library, London

Portrait of John Whyte Melville of Bennochy and Strathkinness,
Captain of the Club 1823 by Sir Francis Grant (1810-1878)
Royal & Ancient Golf Club, St Andrews/Bridgeman Art Library, London

Ladies Match at Westward Ho! by Francis Powell Hopkins (1830-1913)
Private Collection/Bridgeman Art Library, London

Golfing at Westward Ho! by Francis Powell Hopkins (1830-1913)
Private Collection/Bridgeman Art Library, London

Oil Study for Frontispiece of R Clark's 'Golf - A Royal & Ancient Game.' by Clark Stanton (1823-1894)
Private Collection/Bridgeman Art Library, London

View of Military Players at St Andrews, late 17th century English School (17th century),
Royal & Ancient Golf Club, St Andrews
© Phaidon Press Ltd/David Cripps/Brigeman Art Library, London

Other illustrations © Robert Frederick Archives